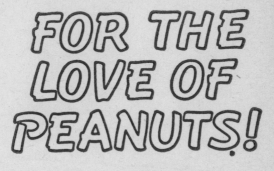

FOR THE LOVE OF PEANUTS!

by Charles M. Schulz

Selected cartoons from
Good Grief, More Peanuts!
Vol. II

A Fawcett Crest Book

Fawcett Publications, Inc., Greenwich, Connecticut
Member of American Book Publishers Council, Inc.

This book, prepared especially for Fawcett Publications, Inc.,
comprises the second half of GOOD GRIEF, MORE PEANUTS!,
and is published by arrangement with Holt, Rinehart and
Winston, Inc.

Thirteenth Fawcett Crest printing, March 1968

Published by Fawcett World Library,
67 West 44th Street, New York, New York 10036.
Printed in the United States of America

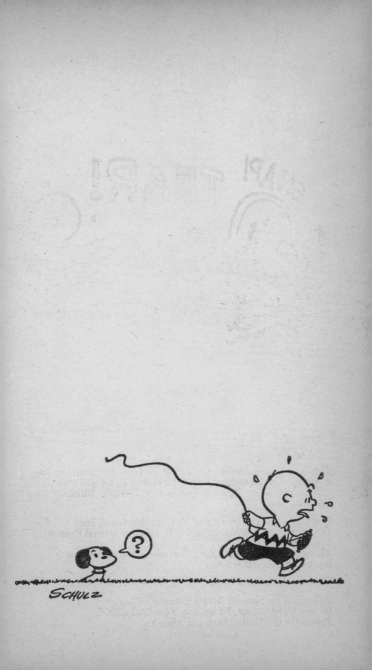

THUMP THUMP THUMP THUMP

KLUNK!

DON'T PANIC!

THERE ARE ENOUGH PEANUTS TO GO AROUND!

LOOK FOR THE PEANUTS CARTOON BOOKS
IN THE NEW CREST EDITIONS

k947	HERE COMES SNOOPY	**k858**	GOOD GRIEF, CHARLIE BROWN!
k907	YOU ARE TOO MUCH, CHARLIE BROWN	**k854**	HEY, PEANUTS!
k884	WE'RE ON YOUR SIDE, CHARLIE BROWN	**k831**	FOR THE LOVE OF PEANUTS!
k875	THE WONDERFUL WORLD OF PEANUTS	**k818**	WHAT NEXT, CHARLIE BROWN!
k871	FUN WITH PEANUTS		
k870	HERE COMES CHARLIE BROWN!	**k945**	VERY FUNNY, CHARLIE BROWN

Hey, wait for me—good grief!

On Sale Wherever Paperbacks Are Sold—Only **40¢** each

FAWCETT WORLD LIBRARY